Easy Learning

Maths

Age 9–10

My name is ....

I am .... years old.

I go to .... School.

My birthday is ....

Peter Clarke

How to use this book

- Find a quiet, comfortable place to work, away from other distractions.

- Ask your child what maths they are doing at school and choose an appropriate topic.

- Tackle one topic at a time.

- Help with reading the instructions where necessary, and ensure that your child understands what to do.

- Help and encourage your child to check their own answers as they complete each activity.

- Discuss with your child what they have learnt.

- Let your child return to their favourite pages once they have been completed, to play the games and talk about the activities.

- Reward your child with plenty of praise and encouragement.

Special features

- Games: There is a game on each double page, which reinforces the maths topic. Some of the games require a spinner. This is easily made using a pencil, a paperclip and the circle printed on each games page. Gently flick the paperclip with your finger to make it spin.

- Parent's notes: These are divided into 'What you need to know', which explain the key maths idea, and 'Taking it further', which suggest activities and encourage discussion with your child about what they have learnt. The words in bold are key words that you should focus on when talking to your child.

Published by Collins
An imprint of HarperCollins*Publishers*
77–85 Fulham Palace Road
Hammersmith
London
W6 8JB

Browse the complete Collins catalogue at
www.collins.co.uk

First published in 2006
© HarperCollins*Publishers* 2008

10 9 8 7 6 5 4 3 2 1

ISBN-13 978-0-00-730102-7

British Library Cataloguing in Publication Data
A Catalogue record for this publication is available from the British Library

Written by Peter Clarke
Design and layout by Lodestone Publishing Limited, Uckfield, East Sussex; www.lodestonepublishing.com
Illustrated by Rachel Annie Bridgen;
www.shootingthelight.com
Cover design by Susi Martin
Cover illustration by John Haslam
Printed and bound by Martins the Printers Ltd

Contents

Positive and negative numbers

Large numbers

- Write these as numbers.

  sixty-three thousand, four hundred and eight

  eight thousand, two hundred and seventeen

  two hundred and sixty-eight thousand

  one hundred and four thousand, six hundred and thirty-nine

- Write these as words.

  509 217

  38 001

  742 358

  6608

Comparing numbers

- Order these numbers, least first.

12	8	–8	–12	11	–10
–6	–5	–8	–1	–3	–10
2	–1	–3	0	4	–5

- Write the number that each arrow points to.

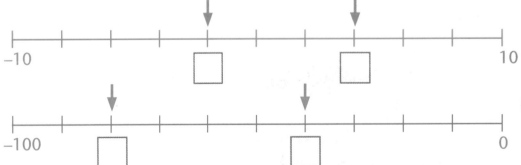

What you need to know At this stage your child is learning to **read**, **write** and **order** any **whole number**, including **negative numbers**. It is useful for your child to see negative numbers in a context, e.g. as a temperature, or as numbers positioned on a number line.

Game: Ordering numbers

You need: 8 counters (or buttons), 2 pencils, 2 pieces of paper.

- Take turns to put a counter above either a racing car or a speedboat.
- Once all 8 counters have been used, write the numbers in order, starting with the smallest.
- The first player to order the 8 numbers correctly wins 1 point.
- Remove all the counters and repeat. The winner is the first player to win 5 points.

Different orders

-5   -3   1   4

- Write numbers for each of the blank cards so that the 7 numbers are in order.
- How many different ways can you think of?

Taking it further   Look for large numbers, e.g. in newspapers, TV guides, on food packaging. Ask your child to say the **number** and write it in **words**. Choose several large numbers and ask your child to **order** the numbers. Say a large number, e.g. four hundred and sixteen thousand, eight hundred and twenty-three, and ask your child to write the number in **figures**.

Multiplying and dividing by 10 and 100

Multiplying by 10 and 100

• Multiply each of these by 10.

• Multiply each of these by 100.

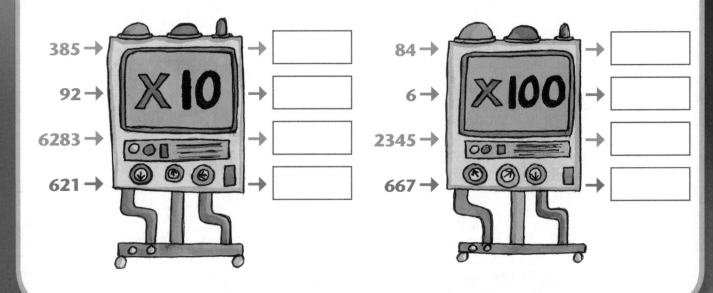

385 →

92 →

6283 →

621 →

84 →

6 →

2345 →

667 →

Dividing by 10 and 100

• Divide each of these by 10.

• Divide each of these by 100.

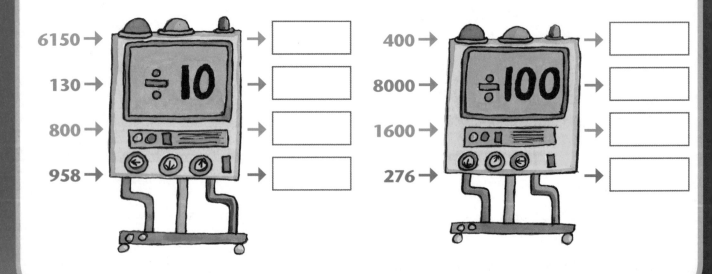

6150 →

130 →

800 →

958 →

400 →

8000 →

1600 →

276 →

What you need to know At this stage your child is learning to **multiply** and **divide** any **number** up to 10 000 by 10 and 100 and understand the effect. It is important that your child understands how **digits** move:
• one place to the **left** when multiplied by 10   • two places to the left when **multiplied** by 100
• one place to the **right** when divided by 10   • two places to the right when **divided** by 100.
This will help them with their work on **decimal** numbers.

3412   85   645   6   27   251   48   7215   9

÷100   x10

÷10   x100

You need: 40 counters or buttons (20 of one colour, 20 of another), paperclip, pencil.

- Take turns to choose a number from the top of the machine, spin the spinner (see page 2) and do the calculation.

- If the answer appears on the grid, cover it with one of your counters. If the number is already covered, miss a turn.

- The winner is the first player to complete a row, column or diagonal of 4 numbers.

60	270	6450	0·27	8500	0·6
0·48	0·85	25·1	34·12	721·5	4·8
341 200	72·15	2·7	4800	2700	34 120
90	0·06	480	6·45	8·5	2·51
64·5	72 150	341·2	25 100	0·9	0·09
2510	850	900	600	721 500	64 500

Making numbers

- Use the three digits below to make fifteen 1-, 2- or 3-digit numbers. You can only use each digit once in each number.

- Multiply and divide each number by 10 and 100.

5

8

3

Taking it further   Look for 1-, 2-, 3- or 4-digit numbers, e.g. in newspapers, TV guides, on food packaging. Ask your child to **multiply** and **divide** each **number** by 10 and 100. Encourage them to explain their thinking, especially when the answer results in a **decimal** number.

Decimals

- What is the value of the red digit in each of these decimal numbers?

  3·58 [ ]   15·87 [ ]   8·46 [ ]

  0·69 [ ]   21·49 [ ]   18·61 [ ]

- Complete these patterns.

  5·6   5·8   6   [ ] [ ] [ ] [ ] [ ]

  4·24   [ ]   4·26   [ ] [ ]   4·29   [ ] [ ]

  [ ]   7·06   [ ]   7·26   [ ] [ ]   7·56   [ ]

Ordering and rounding

- Write these decimal numbers in order starting with the smallest.

  5·3   6·7   2·03   9·5   5·25

  9·73   2·13   6·37   5·94   2·3

  [ ] [ ] [ ] [ ] [ ] [ ] [ ] [ ] [ ] [ ]

- Now round each of the decimal numbers to the nearest whole number.

  [ ]   [ ]   [ ]   [ ]   [ ]

  [ ]   [ ]   [ ]   [ ]   [ ]

What you need to know   At this stage your child is learning to:

- use **decimal notation** for **tenths** (1 decimal place), e.g. 0·5, 3·5 and **hundredths** (2 decimal places), e.g. 0·34, 5·72
- know what each **digit** stands for in numbers with one or two **decimal places**, e.g. 5·8 = 5 **units** (or **ones**) and 8 tenths; 4·26 = 4 units (or ones), 2 tenths and 6 hundredths
- **order** a set of numbers with **one** or **two decimal places**
- **round** a number with one or two decimal places to the **nearest whole number**.

Game: Round to a whole number

You need: paperclip, pencil, 22 counters (or buttons).

- Take turns to spin the spinner twice (see page 2) and make a decimal number, e.g. spin 4 and 7 to make either 4·7 or 7·4.

- Round the decimal number to the nearest whole number, e.g. 4·7 is 5, or 7·4 is 7, and place a counter in the corresponding arch. One player covers the numbers in the top arches and the other player covers the numbers in the bottom arches.

- The winner is the first player to place a counter in each of their 11 arches.

Variation

- Spin the spinner 3 times and make a decimal number with 2 decimal places, e.g. spin 3, 6 and 7 to make 3·67, 3·76, 6·37, 6·73, 7·36 or 7·63, and round each decimal number to the nearest whole number.

Making decimals

Jolly Joke

Why was the teacher so bad at teaching decimals?

He couldn't get the point across!

- Spin the spinner three times. After each spin, write down the number.

- Use the three numbers to make as many different decimal numbers as you can. Use decimal numbers with 1 (tenths) and 2 (hundredths) decimal places.

- Order your decimals smallest to largest.

- Now round each decimal number to the nearest whole number.

Taking it further   Choose a **number** between 1 and 10 with **one decimal place**, e.g. 6·4. Challenge your child to find your number by asking you questions, e.g. 'Is the number **more than** a 3? Is it **between** 4 and 7?' You can only answer Yes or No. Keep a record of how many questions were asked. Repeat several times aiming to reduce the number of questions. Then let your child choose a mystery number for you to guess. Extend by choosing a number with **two decimal places** between 1 and 10, e.g. 3·82.

Fractions and decimals

Fractions and division

- Draw lines to join equivalent statements.

$\frac{1}{2} \times 10$ $\qquad$ $\frac{100}{5}$ $\qquad$ $\frac{1}{4} \times 80$ $\qquad$ $\frac{1}{5} \times 30$ $\qquad$ $\frac{80}{20}$

$100 \div 5$ $\qquad$ $80 \div 20$ $\qquad$ $10 \div 2$ $\qquad$ $80 \div 4$ $\qquad$ $30 \div 5$

- Write each of these as a division calculation. Then work out the answer.

$\frac{1}{4} \times 20$ = [ ] = [ ]

$\frac{18}{6}$ = [ ] = [ ]

$\frac{1}{10} \times 400$ = [ ] = [ ]

$\frac{80}{10}$ = [ ] = [ ]

Fractions and decimals

- Write each of these as a decimal.

$\frac{3}{4}$ [ ] $\qquad$ $\frac{7}{10}$ [ ] $\qquad$ $5\frac{6}{100}$ [ ] $\qquad$ $3\frac{9}{10}$ [ ]

- Write each of these as a fraction.

0.5 [ ] $\qquad$ 0.08 [ ] $\qquad$ 6.71 [ ] $\qquad$ 4.3 [ ]

What you need to know At this stage your child is learning to relate:
- **fractions** to **division** and use division to find simple fractions, including **tenths** and **hundredths**, of numbers and quantities, e.g. $\frac{3}{4}$ of 12, $\frac{1}{10}$ of 50, $\frac{1}{100}$ of £5
- fractions to their decimal **equivalents**, e.g. $\frac{1}{2} = 0.5$, $\frac{6}{10} = 0.6$.

Game: Fractions of amounts

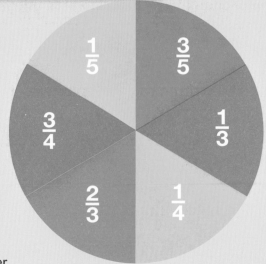

You need: 16 counters (or buttons), paperclip, 2 pencils, 2 pieces of paper.

- Take turns to spin the spinner (see page 2), e.g. $\frac{1}{4}$, and then place a counter on one of the tickets, e.g. Row C Seat 20.

- Using the number on the ticket, work out the answer to the calculation, e.g. $\frac{1}{4}$ x 20 = 5.

- The answer becomes your score for that round. If you cannot work out the answer, or the answer is not a whole number, score 0.

- Once all the tickets have been covered with a counter, each player adds up their scores. The winner is the player with the greater total.

Row B Seat 12	Row G Seat 9	Row E Seat 15	Row A Seat 6
Row D Seat 50	Row J Seat 24	Row D Seat 30	Row F Seat 8
Row J Seat 16	Row K Seat 40	Row B Seat 18	Row D Seat 36
Row C Seat 20	Row A Seat 32	Row G Seat 10	Row H Seat 25

Jolly Joke

How far open were the windows in the maths lesson?

Just a fraction!

Pairs that total 1

- Pair these fractions and decimals so that each pair has a total of 1.

$\frac{1}{5}$	0·25	0·4	$\frac{3}{10}$
0·7	$\frac{3}{5}$	$\frac{3}{4}$	0·8

Taking it further Point to any **fraction** on these pages and ask your child to tell you the **equivalent decimal**. Point to any **decimal** and ask your child to tell you the **equivalent fraction**. Point to one of the fractions on the spinner and a number on one of the tickets, and ask your child to work out that fraction of the number. Only ask questions that give whole number answers, e.g. $\frac{3}{5}$ of 20, not $\frac{2}{3}$ of 20. Encourage them to explain their thinking.

Pencil and paper addition

Adding pairs of numbers

- Use a written method to answer these calculations. Question 1 has been done for you.

1. 4217 + 3728 =

```
  4217
+ 3728
------
  7945
    1
```

2. 3592 + 5772 =

3. 1057 + 2769 =

4. 2413 + 3006 =

5. 1748 + 2933 =

6. 5806 + 452 =

7. 7339 + 1764 =

8. 926 + 914 =

9. 6120 + 2444 =

Are you right?

- Write the digits of each of your answers to the 9 questions above in the table opposite to check them, using the following method. Question 1 has been done for you.

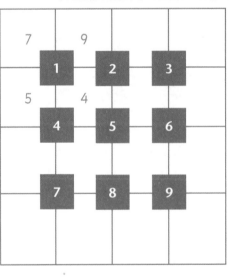

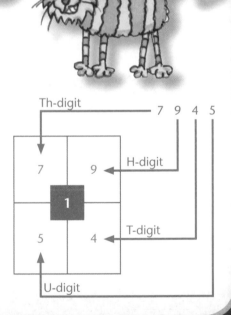

What you need to know When your child is not confident that they can **add** 2- and 3-digit numbers **mentally**, or with the help of **jottings**, encourage them to set out the **calculation** in a **column format**. This **written method** is used on these pages to add together two numbers less than 10 000.

Game: Larger total wins

You need: paperclip, 2 pencils, 2 pieces of paper.

- Take turns to spin the spinner 6 times (see page 2). Write down the number each time you spin so you don't forget the numbers, e.g. 6, 2, 8, 2, 9, 1.

- Use the 6 digits to make a pair of 3-digit numbers, e.g. 962 and 821, and add the two numbers together.

- The winner is the player with the larger total.

- Play 5 rounds. The overall winner is the player who wins more rounds.

Jamie

Round 1
5, 3, 6, 4, 5, 8

Round 2
3, 5, 9,

```
  865
+ 543
 1408
    1
```

Anna

Round 1
6, 2, 8, 2, 9, 1

Round 2
6, 8, 4, 6, 7, 1

```
  962
+ 821
 1783
```

```
  876
+ 641
 1517
    1
```

Jolly Joke

What did one pencil say to the other?

You're looking sharp!

Palindromic additions

The digits in a palindromic number read the same backwards as forwards.

- Write down a 3-digit number. Reverse the digits. Add the two numbers together. Reverse the digits in the answer, and add these two numbers together. This makes a palindromic number in two calculations.

- Investigate other 3-digit numbers.

```
  568        1433
+ 865      + 3341
 1433        4774
```

Taking it further Ask your child to write down your home telephone number, excluding the area code. Make a **4-digit** and a **3-digit** number, e.g. 2576 and 928, or a pair of 3-digit numbers, e.g. 576 and 928. Now ask your child to **add** the two numbers **together**. Repeat for other telephone numbers your child may know or choose numbers from a telephone directory. What if you used mobile phone numbers instead?

Pencil and paper subtraction

Colour subtractions

- Match the colours and use the two numbers for your subtraction.
  Use a written method to answer each calculation.

2596	1853	468	5804	8118

6805	824	3224	4801

Make your own

- Choose any pairs of numbers and write them in the boxes to make each calculation correct.

☐ – ☐ =   ☐ – ☐ =

What you need to know When your child is not confident that they can **subtract** 2- and 3-digit numbers **mentally**, or with the help of **jottings**, encourage them to set out the **calculation** in a **column format**. This **written method** is used on these two pages to subtract two numbers less than 10 000.

Game: Countdown 5000

You need: paperclip, 2 pencils, 2 pieces of paper.

- Each player writes 5000 at the top of their sheet of paper.

- Take turns to spin the spinner 3 times (see page 2) to make a 3-digit number. Subtract this from 5000.

- Continue like this, subtracting each new 3-digit number from the previous answer.

- The aim is to get as close to zero as possible without going below it. At any time you can choose to stop at the answer you have reached. The other player however, can continue.

- The winner is the player who gets as close to, but not below, zero.

- Play 3 rounds. The overall winner is the player who wins more rounds.

Subtraction puzzles

Jolly Joke

Why did the golfer wear 2 jumpers?

In case he got a hole in one!

- Using each of the digits 1 to 9 only once, make the calculation correct.

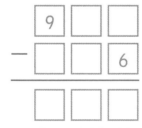

- A 3-digit number is subtracted from a number made up of the same three digits in reverse order. The answer has the same three digits in it, but in another different order. What is the calculation?

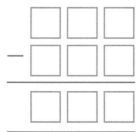

Taking it further   Ask your child to write down 3 or 4 1-digit numbers, e.g. 5, 7 and 9. Arrange the digits to make a pair of **3-** or **4-digit** numbers, e.g. 795 and 597. Now ask your child to find the **difference between** the two numbers. Repeat.

Multiplication facts

Multiplication riddle

How did the tap dancer break his leg?

- Work out the answers to these multiplication facts.

1. 6 x 3 =	**2.** 4 x 9 =	**3.** 7 x 6 =	**4.** 6 x 6 =
5. 4 x 3 =	**6.** 2 x 6 =	**7.** 8 x 2 =	**8.** 4 x 10 =
9. 4 x 6 =	**10.** 7 x 9 =	**11.** 8 x 3 =	**12.** 9 x 2 =
13. 9 x 4 =	**14.** 3 x 9 =	**15.** 4 x 4 =	**16.** 5 x 8 =
17. 7 x 5 =			

Break the code

- Now use your answers from the questions above and the code below to work out the answer to the riddle.

A	B	C	D	E	F	G	H	I	J	K	L	M
64	28	8	14	36	42	49	18	16	10	35	12	20

N	O	P	Q	R	S	T	U	V	W	X	Y	Z
40	63	81	30	32	27	24	100	6	56	48	4	25

1 2   3 4 5 6   7 8 9 10   11 12 13   14 15 16 17

What you need to know It is important at this stage that your child is beginning to know by heart all the **multiplication** facts up to 10 x 10. This will help your child to work out related division facts, e.g. 8 x 6 = 48 and 6 x 8 = 48, so 48 ÷ 6 = 8 and 48 ÷ 8 = 6. **Counting on** and **back** in steps of 2, 3, 4, 5, 6, 7, 8, 9 and 10 helps your child to remember the **multiples** of all the times tables up to 10 x 10.

Game: Multiplication cards

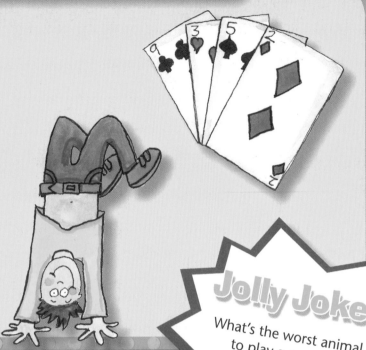

You need: pack of playing cards with the picture cards removed.

- Shuffle the cards and place them face down in a pile in the middle of the table.

- Take turns to pick up the top two cards and multiply the two numbers together.

- The winner of the round is the player with the greater product. The winner collects all four cards.

- Continue to pick up two cards each, and multiply the two numbers together.

- When all the cards have been used, the winner is the player who has collected more cards.

Jolly Joke

What's the worst animal to play a game of cards with?

A cheetah!

Multiplication grid

- Complete this multiplication grid.

x	1	2	3	4	5	6	7	8	9	10
1										
2										
3		6								
4										40
5										
6										
7					35					
8										
9										
10										

Remember:
for each multiplication fact there is another related fact, e.g. 4 x 6 is the same as 6 x 4.
How many facts do you know by heart? Are you surprised how few facts are left?

Taking it further Say together the seven **times table** forwards, then backwards. Ask: 'What are five sevens? How many sevens in 56? Seven **times** three? Forty-two **divided by** seven? Three **multiplied** by seven is…? Seven times what **equals** seventy?' Repeat for other times tables.

Short multiplication

Multiplication calculations

● Use a written method to answer these calculations.

268 x 7 = ☐

472 x 9 = ☐

673 x 8 = ☐

514 x 6 = ☐

807 x 5 = ☐

786 x 4 = ☐

Making multiplications

● Arrange each set of 4 digits to make a 3-digit and a 1-digit number, then use a written method to answer each calculation.

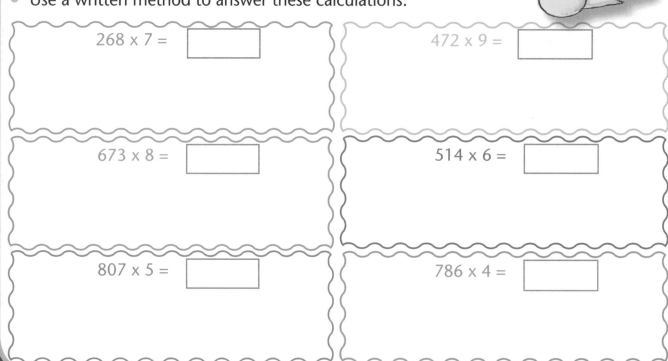

6, 4, 2, 9 ☐☐☐ x ☐ =   3, 5, 1, 8 ☐☐☐ x ☐ =

5, 2, 7, 3 ☐☐☐ x ☐ =   4, 9, 6, 8 ☐☐☐ x ☐ =

What you need to know When your child is not confident that they can **multiply** larger numbers **mentally**, or with the help of **jottings**, encourage them to set out the **calculation** in a **column format**. The **written methods** used on these pages involve **short multiplication** of a 3-digit number by a single-digit number, e.g. 674 x 9.

Game: Target 3000

You need: pack of playing cards with the picture cards removed, 2 pencils, 2 pieces of paper, 5 counters (or buttons).

- Shuffle the cards and place them face down in a pile in the middle of the table.

- Take turns to pick up the top five cards. Choose four of the cards and arrange them into a 3-digit by 1-digit multiplication calculation, discarding the card that seems least useful.

- The player with the product closer to 3000 is the winner of that round and collects a counter.

- Collect all the cards, shuffle, and repeat. The overall winner is the player with more counters after five rounds.

Jolly Joke

What type of painting do maths teachers most enjoy?

Painting by numbers!

Making more multiplications

- Write down any four digits, e.g. 3, 5, 7 and 8, and make a 3-digit number and a 1-digit number. Multiply the two numbers together.

- By re-arranging the four digits, investigate what other products you can make by multiplying a 3-digit number by a 1-digit number. What is the largest/smallest answer you can make?

Taking it further   Ask your child to write down a **3-digit number** and a **1-digit** number, e.g. 476 and 4. Then ask them to **estimate** the **product** of these two numbers. Ask: 'If you **multiply** 476 by 4, **approximately** what is the answer? How did you get that **approximation**? What digit will be in the units place? Why?' Then ask your child to calculate the answer, either **mentally**, mentally with **jottings**, or using a **written method**. Ask: 'How did you work it out? What other method could you have used to work it out?'

Long multiplication

Remember   28 x 46 →

	20	8
40	800	320
6	120	48

```
 800
 320
 120
+ 48
1288
```

or

```
   28
 x 46
 1120    40 x 28
  168     6 x 28
 1288
```

Multiplication puzzles

- Solve these multiplication puzzles using a written method.

Multiply the sum of 12 and 16 by the sum of 39 and 28.

Multiply the sum of 54 and 33 by the sum of 17 and 17.

Multiply the difference between 78 and 26 by the difference between 60 and 15.

Multiply the difference between 58 and 22 by the difference between 97 and 24.

Multiply the sum of 57 and 12 by the difference between 95 and 21.

Multiply the sum of 25 and 24 by the difference between 88 and 33.

Making even more multiplications

- Write a different two-digit number in each circle and then write the answer in the rectangle.

47 x 〇 = [   ]   52 x 〇 = [   ]

〇 x 83 = [   ]   〇 x 76 = [   ]

What you need to know   When your child is not confident that they can **multiply** larger numbers **mentally**, or with the help of **jottings**, encourage them to set out the **calculation** in a **column format**. The **written methods** used on these pages involve **long multiplication** of a pair of two-digit numbers, e.g. 47 x 83.

Game: Estimating products

You need: 10 counters (or buttons), 2 pencils, 2 pieces of paper.

- Both players place a counter on one of the sailing boats.

- Each player writes down an estimate of the product of these two numbers.

- Each player then calculates the answer and checks to see that they both have the same answer.

- The winner is the player whose estimate is closer to the actual answer.

- The overall winner is the player who wins more rounds after counters have been placed on all the sailing boats.

Jolly Joke

What is one of the longest words?

Smile: because it has a mile in it!

More multiplication puzzles

- Using each of the digits 1, 3, 5, 7 and 9 only once, make a calculation where the answer is 2222.

$$\boxed{}\boxed{} \times \boxed{}\boxed{} - \boxed{} = 2222$$

Can you do it another way?

Hint
The smallest digit is the one-digit number!

- Put the following numbers into three sets of three numbers so that the product of each set is 840.

3	4	5	6	7	8	28	30	35

Taking it further Ask your child to write down a pair of **2-digit numbers**, e.g. 29 and 67. Ask: 'How would you work out what 29 **multiplied by** 67 is? Is there another way you could work it out?' Encourage your child to explain to you the different methods they could use to work out the **answer**. Then ask: 'What do you think is the **approximate** answer?' Next ask your child to calculate the answer. Finally ask: 'How did you work it out? Is your answer correct? How do you know? How close was your **approximation**?'

Short division

Division calculations

- Use a written method to answer these calculations.

537 ÷ 7 = ☐

407 ÷ 5 = ☐

763 ÷ 9 = ☐

629 ÷ 4 = ☐

822 ÷ 6 = ☐

314 ÷ 8 = ☐

Making divisions

- Join a 3-digit number to a 1-digit number, then use a written method to answer each calculation.

564   307   928   778

6   8   3   7

☐ ÷ ☐ = ⬭   ☐ ÷ ☐ = ⬭

☐ ÷ ☐ = ⬭   ☐ ÷ ☐ = ⬭

What you need to know When your child is not confident that they can **divide** larger numbers **mentally**, or with the help of **jottings**, encourage them to set out the **calculation** in a **column format**. The **written methods** used on these pages involve **short division** of a three-digit number by a single-digit number, e.g. 678 ÷ 6.

Game: 4-spin division

You need: paperclip, 2 pencils, 2 pieces of paper.

- Take turns to spin the spinner (see page 2) 4 times. Write down the number each time you spin so you don't forget the numbers!

- Arrange the 4 numbers to make a 3-digit and a 1-digit number.

- Divide the 3-digit number by the 1-digit number.

- The winner is the player with the lower answer.

- Play 5 rounds. The overall winner is the player who wins more rounds.

$$3, 6, 4, 5 \qquad 345 \div 6 =$$

$$\begin{array}{r} 57 \quad r \ 3 \\ 6 \ \overline{)\ 345} \\ -\ 300 \\ \hline 45 \\ -\ 42 \\ \hline 3 \end{array}$$

$$50 \times 6$$

$$7 \times 6$$

Target 158

- Using each of the digits above only once, make a 3-digit and a 1-digit number where the answer is 158 when you divide the 3-digit number by the 1-digit number.

- Now try using these digits.

Taking it further Ask your child to write down a 3-**digit number** and a 1-digit number, e.g. 548 and 7. Ask: 'How would you work out what 548 **divided by** 7 is? Is there another way you could work it out?' Encourage your child to explain to you the different methods they could use to work out the **answer**. Then ask: 'What do you think is the **approximate** answer?' Next ask your child to calculate the answer. Finally ask: 'How did you work it out? Is your answer correct? How do you know? How close was your **approximation**?'

Money

Money calculations

- Answer these.

| £3.24 | £2.16 | £3.45 | | £3.27 | £1.49 | £7.72 | | £8.91 | £7.63 | £9.15 |

Total ☐

Change from £10 ☐

Total ☐

Change from £20 ☐

Total ☐

Change from £50 ☐

- Find the cost of each of these.

2 oranges £1.30

4 apples £2

3 bananas £1.80

1 peach 80p

6 melons £7.20

1 pear 75p

1 melon ☐

5 pears ☐

3 apples ☐

1 banana ☐

4 oranges ☐

6 peaches ☐

Money percentages

- Answer these.

10% of £4 = ☐

80% of £100 = ☐

50% of £80 = ☐

20% of £5 = ☐

25% of £10 = ☐

5% of £4 = ☐

What you need to know   At this stage your child is learning to:
- find **totals** and give **change** using **pounds** and **pence**
- find simple **percentages** involving **money**
- solve problems involving money
- make simple **conversions** from pounds to **foreign currency**.

Game: Make £26

You need: paperclip, 2 pencils, 2 pieces of paper.

- Take turns to spin the spinner (see page 2), e.g. 5%.
- Then choose one of the notes or coins, e.g. £50, and calculate the answer, e.g. 5% of £50 = £2.50
- Keep a running total. The winner is the first player to make exactly £26.

Variation

- Try making other amounts, e.g. £18, £30, £48...

50%	1%
20%	2%
10%	5%

Foreign currency

- Calculate how much money you would get for £10 in Europe, the USA, Switzerland, Australia and Japan.
- How much money would you get for £5 in each of these countries?

Exchange rates for £1 are approximately:

Euro (€)	1.4
USA Dollar ($)	1.7
Swiss Franc (Fr)	2.25
Australian Dollar ($)	2.2
Japanese Yen (Y)	193

Taking it further While shopping, point out an item costing less than £1. Ask your child to **estimate**, then work out in their head the **cost** of four of these items. See how close they come. Also, if you see any items labelled, e.g. '2 for £3.20', ask them to work out the cost of one item for you, and to explain how they got the answer. Also encourage your child to say how much change you would receive for that item if you offered, e.g. £5 or £10.

Area and perimeter

Area and perimeter calculations

● Calculate the area and perimeter of each rectangle.

8 m x 10 m

Area

Perimeter

16 m x 24 m

Area

Perimeter

15 m x 40 m

Area

Perimeter

12 m x 10 m

Area

Perimeter

9 m x 6 m

Area

Perimeter

14 m x 24 m

Area

Perimeter

What you need to know At this stage your children is learning to:
- understand **perimeter** as the **boundary** of a shape
- measure and calculate perimeters of rectangles
- understand **area** as the total **surface** of a shape within its boundary
- use the formula in words '**length x breadth**' for the area of a rectangle and record measurements in **square centimetres (cm²)** or **square metres (m²)**.

Game: Area and perimeter totals

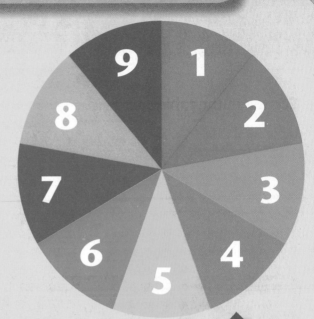

You need: paperclip, 2 pencils, 2 pieces of paper.

- Take turns to spin the spinner twice (see page 2).
- Calculate the perimeter and area of a rectangle with those measurements.
- Keep a running total.
- The winner is the first player to have a total perimeter greater than 100 units, and a total area greater than 200 units^2.

4 and 8
Perimeter = 24 units
Area = 32 units^2

Toothpick areas

Jolly Joke

Where are teachers made?

On an assembly line!

- Arrange 12 toothpicks (or pencils) as shown with an area of nine squares.
- Now rearrange them to make shapes with areas of 8, 7, 6, 5, 4 and 3 squares.

Taking it further Find a ruler, pencil and some used envelopes of different sizes. Choose one of the envelopes and ask your child to **estimate** its **perimeter** to the nearest **centimetre** and write their estimate on the back. Now ask your child to **measure** the envelope and write the **actual** perimeter next to their estimate. How close was your child's estimate to the actual perimeter? Repeat, choosing other envelopes and asking your child to estimate then work out the perimeter or **area** of each envelope.

Quadrilaterals and triangles

Quadrilaterals

- Complete the table.

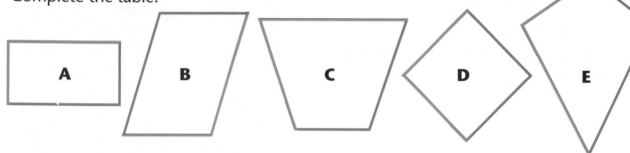

Property	Quadrilateral				
	A	B	C	D	E
All angles are right angles	✔	✘	✘	✔	✘
Opposite sides are equal					
Opposite sides are parallel					
Has 2 or more lines of symmetry					
Diagonals are equal in length					
Diagonals cross at right angles					
Red lines are perpendicular					

Triangles

- Colour all the isosceles triangles red, equilateral triangles green and scalene triangles blue.

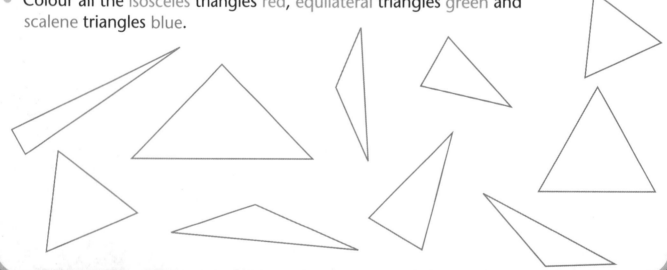

Game: Make a rectangle

You need: 40 counters or buttons (20 of one colour, 20 of another), pencil and paper.

- Take turns to place one of your counters at an intersection on the board.

- The aim is to be the player that places the 4th counter on the board to make a rectangle, e.g. in the black rectangle below, there are already 2 blue counters and 1 green counter on the board. The player that places the 4th counter counts the rectangle as theirs.

- The rectangle can be any orientation or size.

- Keep track of how many rectangles you have made. The winner is the player who makes more rectangles.

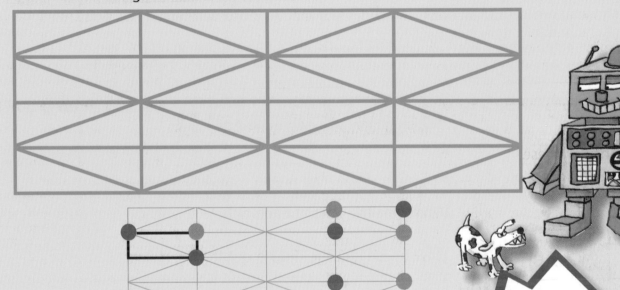

Variation   Play 'Make a triangle'.

Tracing puzzles

- Can you trace over these shapes without lifting your pencil off the sheet?

- You are not allowed to retrace any lines but you can cross over lines.

Taking it further   Point to different shapes in the house, garden and while out shopping. Ask your child to identify **perpendicular** and **parallel lines** in the shapes. Point to different **triangles** and ask your child to classify them as being **isosceles**, **equilateral** or **scalene**.

Word problems

Real life problems

- Answer these.

There are 203 children in 7 classes. The same number of children are in each class. However, today 5 children are away from Year 5. How many children are in Year 5 today?

70 adults and 50 children were asked which car colour they prefer. If 25% of those asked said they preferred red, how many people preferred red cars?

Madeline bought a pack of 30 biscuits. She ate $\frac{1}{5}$ of them on Monday. She ate $\frac{1}{4}$ of the remaining biscuits on Tuesday. How many biscuits did she have left?

Money problems

- Answer these.

A man paid £96 for four football tickets. All tickets were the same price.

What was the cost of each ticket?

How much change did he get from £100?

Petrol costs 92.6p a litre. How much do you pay to fill a 5 litre can?

A CD normally costs £20. It has a 25% discount in a sale. What is the sale price of the CD?

Measures problems

- Answer these.

A recipe needs 25 g of butter, 75 g of sugar, 250 g of flour and 60g of cocoa. What is the total weight of these ingredients?

A full bucket holds $10\frac{1}{2}$ litres. A full jug holds $\frac{1}{2}$ a litre. How many jugs of water will fill the bucket?

Amita travelled 4·6 km by car, 68·5 km by train and 1 km on foot. How many kilometres did Amita travel in total?

What you need to know Solving **problems** in the real world is how most people use and apply their mathematical knowledge. At this stage your child is using **addition**, **subtraction**, **multiplication** and **division** to solve simple word problems involving numbers and quantities based on 'real life', **money** and **measures**, using one or more steps, including finding simple percentages. They are learning to choose the **appropriate operation** and **way to calculate**. It is important that you do not just focus on the answers to the word problems, but talk to your child about the way they work things out.

Game: Making problems

You need: paperclip, 2 pencils, 2 pieces of paper.

- Each player spins all three spinners (see page 2) and thinks of a related word problem, including the answer.

- If you spin a '2 step' problem, both ends of the paperclip in the 'Operation' spinner tell you which operations to use. (So you could get e.g. Steps: 2 step; Context: money; Operation: x and $\frac{1}{2}$, which would be a 2 step money problem involving multiplication and fractions.) NB The $\frac{1}{2}$ on the spinner refers to fractions in general.

- Each player then tells their word problem to the other player.

- Both players then work out the answers.

- Repeat several times.

Spinner (Steps): two step | one step | two step | one step

Steps

Spinner (Operation): $\frac{1}{2}$ | + | % | − | ÷ | x

Operation

Spinner (Context): time | real life | capacity | money | mass | length

Context

Jolly Joke

If it takes 6 men one hour to dig a hole. How long would it take for one man to dig half a hole?

You can't dig half a hole!

Pocket money

- Would you be willing to take just one penny as pocket money this week as long as each week after that the amount of money would double?   Yes   No

- How much pocket money would you get in the 8th week? ☐

- What about the:

  12th week ☐   15th week ☐   20th week ☐   24th week ☐

Taking it further   Find times at home, when out shopping or visiting other places to ask your child a **word problem**. Ask questions that involve **addition**, **subtraction**, **multiplication** and **division**, one or more **steps** and in the context of '**real life**', **money** or **measures**. Ask your child: 'What is the **answer** to this problem? How did you work it out? What did you think about? What **operation** do you need to use: addition, subtraction, multiplication or division? What is the **number sentence**? Is your answer correct? How do you know?'

Answers

Page 4
Large numbers
63 408, 8217, 268 000, 104 639
five hundred and nine thousand,
two hundred and seventeen;
thirty-eight thousand and one;
seven hundred and forty-two thousand,
three hundred and fifty-eight;
six thousand, six hundred and eight

Comparing numbers
−12, −10, −8, 8, 11, 12
−10, −8, −6, −5, −3, −1
−5, −3, −1, 0, 2, 4
Green arrows: −2, 4
Pink arrows: −80, −40

Page 5
Different orders
There are 6 different answers:
−5, −4, −3, −2, 1, 2, 4
−5, −4, −3, −2, 1, 3, 4
−5, −4, −3, −1, 1, 2, 4
−5, −4, −3, −1, 1, 3, 4
−5, −4, −3, 0, 1, 2, 4
−5, −4, −3, 0, 1, 3, 4

Page 6
Multiplying by 10 and 100

3850	8400
920	600
62 830	234 500
6210	667 00

Dividing by 10 and 100

615	4
13	80
80	16
95·8	2·76

Page 7
Making numbers
3: 30, 300, 0·3, 0·03
5: 50, 500, 0·5, 0·05
8: 80, 800, 0·8, 0·08
35: 350, 3500, 3·5, 0·35
38: 380, 3800, 3·8, 0·38
53: 530, 5300, 5·3, 0·53
58: 580, 5800, 5·8, 0·58
83: 830, 8300, 8·3, 0·83
85: 850, 8500, 8·5, 0·85
358: 3580, 35 800, 35·8, 3·58
385: 3850, 38 500, 38·5, 3·85
538: 5380, 53 800, 53·8, 5·38
583: 5830, 58 300, 58·3, 5·83
835: 8350, 83 500, 83·5, 8·35
853: 8530, 85 300, 85·3, 8·53

Page 8
Tenths and hundredths
5 tenths, 7 hundredths, 8 units or
ones, 9 hundredths, 2 tens or 20,
6 tenths
5·6, 5·8, 6, 6·2, 6·4, 6·6, 6·8, 7
4·24, 4·25, 4·26, 4·27, 4·28, 4·29,
4·3, 4·31
6·96, 7·06, 7·16, 7·26, 7·36, 7·46,
7·56, 7·66

Ordering and rounding
2·03, 2·13, 2·3, 5·25, 5·3, 5·94,
6·37, 6·7, 9·5, 9·73
5, 7, 2, 10, 5
10, 2, 6, 6, 2

Page 9
Making decimals
Check your child's answers.

Page 10
Fractions and division

$20 \div 4 = 5$; $18 \div 6 = 3$;
$400 \div 10 = 40$; $80 \div 10 = 8$

Fractions and decimals
0·75, 0·7, 5·06, 3·9
$\frac{1}{2}$, $\frac{8}{100}$, $6\frac{71}{100}$, $4\frac{3}{10}$

Page 11
Pairs that total 1
$\frac{1}{5}$ and 0·8, 0·25 and $\frac{3}{4}$,
0·4 and $\frac{3}{5}$, $\frac{3}{10}$ and 0·7

Page 12
Adding pairs of numbers

2. 9364	3. 3826
4. 5419	5. 4681
6. 6258	7. 9103
8. 1840	9. 8564

Are you right?

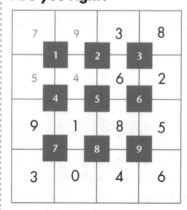

Page 13
Palindromic additions
Check your child's answers.

Page 14
Colour subtractions
$5804 - 3224 = 2580$
$6805 - 2596 = 4209$
$4801 - 1853 = 2948$
$824 - 468 = 356$
$8118 - 5804 = 2314$
$4801 - 824 = 3977$

Make your own
Possible subtractions with
given answers:
$6123 - 3527 = 2596$
$7762 - 957 = 6805$

Page 15
Subtraction puzzles

927 −	954 −
346	459
581	495

Page 16
Multiplication riddle

1. 18	2. 36	3. 42
4. 36	5. 12	6. 12
7. 16	8. 40	9. 24
10. 63	11. 24	12. 18
13. 36	14. 27	15. 16
16. 40	17. 35	

Break the code
He fell into the sink

Page 17
Multiplication grid

x	1	2	3	4	5	6	7	8	9	10
1	1	2	3	4	5	6	7	8	9	10
2	2	4	6	8	10	12	14	16	18	20
3	3	6	9	12	15	18	21	24	27	30
4	4	8	12	16	20	24	28	32	36	40
5	5	10	15	20	25	30	35	40	45	50
6	6	12	18	24	30	36	42	48	54	60
7	7	14	21	28	35	42	49	56	63	70
8	8	16	24	32	40	48	56	64	72	80
9	9	18	27	36	45	54	63	72	81	90
10	10	20	30	40	50	60	70	80	90	100

Page 18
Multiplication calculations
$268 \times 7 = 1876$ $472 \times 9 = 4248$
$673 \times 8 = 5384$ $514 \times 6 = 3084$
$807 \times 5 = 4035$ $786 \times 4 = 3144$